ROOSTER RAG

A cantata in popular style
for unison voices (with divisions) and piano,
with guitar chord symbols

words and music by

MICHAEL HURD

Order No: NOV 200178

NOVELLO PUBLISHING LIMITED
8/9 Frith Street, London W1V 5TZ

For Sara Wood and the Cookham Children

Commissioned by the Cookham Festival, this work received its first performance on 2 May 1975, at the Pinder Hall.

NOTES ON PERFORMANCE

Though *Rooster Rag* was written as a pop cantata to be sung by a chorus throughout, the Cookham premiere in fact presented it as a stage work, in an ingenious and highly effective production by Sara Wood. This is how it was done:

> A Main Chorus sang outside the stage, standing on either side of the proscenium arch. On stage was a chorus of six hens, the main characters — Chanticleer, Pertelote, and Mr Fox — and a Narrator, dressed as the 'Widow' of the first song, who popped in and out of the action as required. Entrances and exits, and all basic action and reaction corresponded to the plan implicit in the lyrics and narration.
>
> Costumes were simple: based on tights and leotards, with appropriate tails and head-dresses. The acting style had a distinct thirties flavour: the hens behaving like a typical boop-a-doop girlie chorus. Actions were mimed and often worked into a dance routine.

All adjustments necessary for a similar stage performance have been incorporated into the present vocal score. A horizontal bracket above the stave indicates that the words and notes beneath are to be sung by someone other than the main singer(s) of the song. The same applies to a handful of the narrator's words. In this edition, from the stage point of view, CHORUS means Main Chorus and Stage Chorus combined. Alternative words (I/We, etc.) have been indicated where necessary.

Rooster Rag can, of course, be performed as a cantata — with or without division into solo, main chorus and semi-chorus effects. And there may well be other ways of presenting it. The thing is to *enjoy* it.

MICHAEL HURD

DURATION ABOUT 13 MINUTES

ROOSTER RAG

MICHAEL HURD

20156

NARRATOR (WIDOW). *1st time* And then, all
2nd time One morning,

the other hens would gather round her and repeat her song:
however, Chanticleer staggered from his bed, bleary-eyed and haggard.

(STAGE CHORUS)
He was a worried man:

Brisk ♩.= 66

(CHANTICLEER)

1 I had a ter-ri-ble dream!____
2 I had a sin-gu-lar fright!____

(STAGE CHORUS)

Woke in the night And my heart went_ Pit-a-pat, pit-a-pat, I am
Tried to es-cape, But my legs turned In-to stone, in-to stone, I was

* pronounce 'sight'.

Means that the fu-ture is ve - ry bright: For - tune's wait - ing

round the cor - ner. Oh what a pros-pect in view!

Some-thing is com-ing That will make you glad. And that is the mean-ing Of the

mean - ing of the dream you've had!_____

NARRATOR (WIDOW). Chanticleer felt much better when he heard these cheering words, for

he knew that Pertelote had a habit of being right about such matters. And so, when he met a rather foxy-looking gentleman with a very red, cunning face, he simply said "Good morning" and (CHANTICLEER)

thought no ill. But the foxy gentleman tapped him
on the shoulder and said:

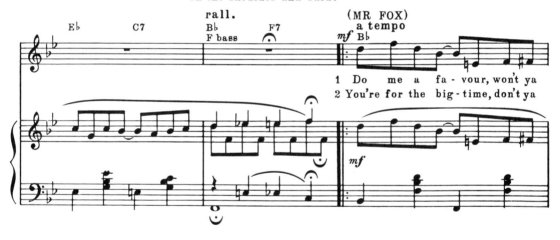

1 Do   me a   fa - vour, won't ya
2 You're for the   big - time, don't ya

Sing me   a   song,— You've got   a   voice in   a   thou - sand, ho - ney—
Know you'll go   far,— You've got the   looks to   go   with— it, ho - ney—

Take my ad - vice, and ba - by You could e - ven Sing in op - 'ra!

(CHORUS)
a tempo

{I / He's} got the con - tacts, yes an' {I know / He knows} the score, This is a

chance in a mil - lion, ho - ney— The tide is turn - in' for ya.

Look at the fu - ture com - in', Ain't it a peach! What - e - ver

dreams you may have Dreamed you're dream-in' Lie with-in reach.

NARRATOR (WIDOW). Chanticleer blushed and flapped his wings. It was true —
he had a fine voice: Everybody said so. If others could win fame and

fortune and glitter, why shouldn't he? So he closed his eyes, stretched out his neck, and began to sing:

Adagio, molto espressivo ♩ = 69
SOLO (CHANTICLEER)

O   for the wings,   for the wings   of a

NARRATOR (WIDOW). And the fox grabbed him.

Harsh and insistent ♩ = 120   (CHORUS I & II)

d...   There's a   thief in the night An' he's

got no pi - ty, There's a thief an' he's com-in' af-ter you. There's a

thief in the night, An' he's in the ci - ty, He has plans for me an'

plans for you. He's snif-fin' a - round! Bolt all the doors and win-dows!

Paw-in' the ground! Put out the light! Don't make a sound! Just pull the blan-kets o-ver!

Who d'you think you're kid-din'? Clo-ser, clo-ser, He is get-ting clo-ser! There's a thief in the night An' it just ain't fun-ny, There's a thief an' he's com-in' af-ter you. There's a thief in the night, An' he don't want mo-ney, 'Cos he knows just what he has to do. He's

night! Here he comes!

Here he comes!

NARRATOR (WIDOW). Off ran the fox, dragging Chanticleer behind him. Off ran the

With a swing ♩ = 90

villagers and the hens, in hot pursuit— but the fox outstripped them all. At last he paused to

take breath, and Chanticleer, realizing that this would be his last chance, whispered to him

as best he could:

Cheerfully ♩=104
(1st time CHANTICLEER, 2nd time CHORUS)

1 If I were you, Do you know what I'd do? I'd
I'd the luck, To have your kind of pluck, I'd

sing and dance and laugh and shout, I'd point my tri-umph out, If I were you.
let them know just what was what, I would-n't care a jot, If I'd your pluck.

If I'd my way, Do you know what I'd say? I'd
If I'd the nerve, And had your kind of verve, I'd

stand and shout de - fi - ance at Each brick and stone and bat, If I'd my
make it plain as plain could be They'd nev - er cap-ture me, If I'd the

segue

NARRATOR (WIDOW). This time it was the fox who fell into the trap. He opened his mouth—

and Chanticleer escaped onto the highest branch of a nearby tree — and nothing the fox could

do or say would make him budge. Of course, in the end, Chanticleer was rescued by his friends

and the fox crept back to his lair, furious at the way things had turned out. And that is the end

of the story — except, of course, for the moral:

care! And don't give house-room to flat-te-ry. _ Be-
ware! Take care! When you feel pride swell-ing
up in-side, You may be sure That you're A-bout to sign a-way dis-cre-tion, And you're
climb-ing up the lad-der On the dan-ger list, This is the mo-ment to be-
ware! Be-ware! Take care! And don't give in to ca-

Printed and bound in Great Britain by
Caligraving Limited Thetford Norfolk